Buzzy Bee's 123

by Miriam Moss

MACDONALD YOUNG BOOKS

1 bee went buzzing...

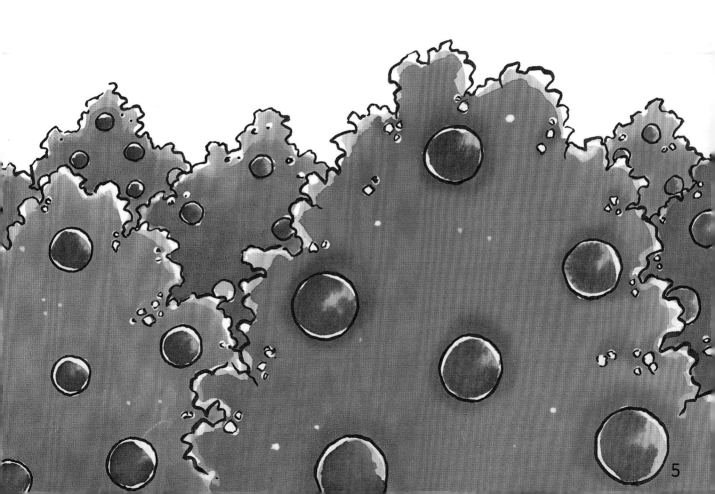

2 worms went wiggling.

Where are you going you wet, wiggling worms?

3 spiders went spinning.

Where are you going,
you silk-spinning spiders?

4 beetles went diving.

Where are you going, you dip-diving beetles?

5 snails went sliding.

Where are you going, you slip-sliding snails?

Shh!

6 butterflies went fluttering.

Where are you going, you
flit-fluttering butterflies?

7 slugs went sliming.

Where are you going, you slow, sliming slugs?

8 caterpillars went looping.

Where are you going,
you hoop-looping
caterpillars?

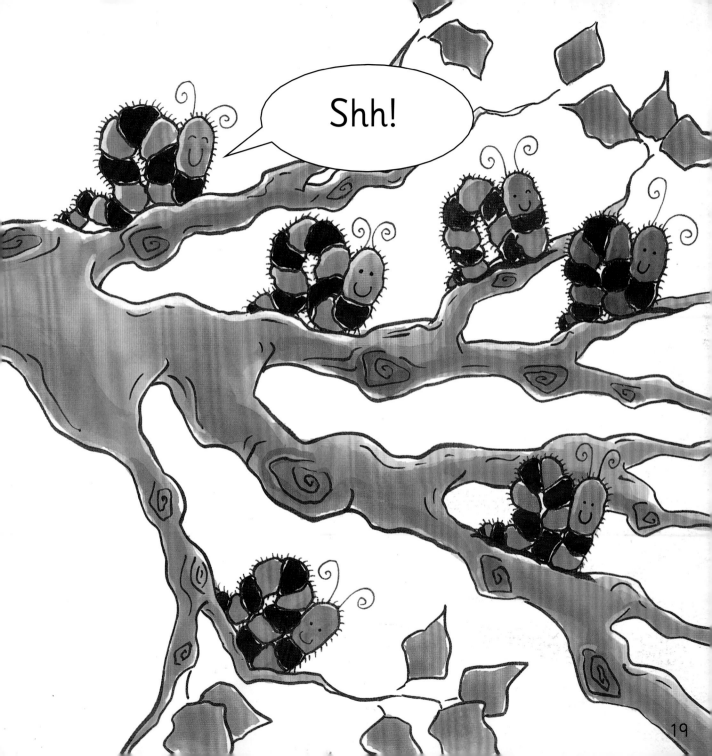

9 ants went tramping.

Where are you going,
you stamp-tramping ants?

Shh!